What's so **Funny** about long-term care?

Also By Patt Schwab

Leave a Mark, Not a Stain!
What Every Manager Needs to Know about Using Humor in the Workplace

Humor Us
America's Funniest Humorists on the Power of Laughter

Creating a Legacy of Laughter
60 Easy Ways to Add Humor to Your Daily Life

What if the Hokey Pokey IS What It's All About?
A Workbook for Writing the Next Chapter of Your Life

What's so Funny about long-term care?

Tips, ideas, and examples of
how patients and caregivers find

Humor in long-term care

PATT SCHWAB, PH.D.

Published by Rollingwood Press
9401 45th Ave. NE
Seattle, WA 98115

Printed in the United States of America

Editing and layout by Christine Dubois
Cover design by Gretchen Flickinger

ISBN: 1-59872-527-0

Order Information:

To order additional copies of this book or to ask about the other products and services offered by Dr. Patt Schwab, contact: www.Fundamentallyspeaking.com

Laughter is the Catharsis that Lets us Keep on Caring

Years ago I spoke to the Emergency Room staff at Harborview Medical Center, the largest trauma facility in the Pacific Northwest. My speech, on workplace humor, immediately followed an hour-and-a-half presentation on "Domestic Violence and How to Recognize It in the ER." Not the ideal spot for a humor speech!

I turned to Judy Wishman, the ER Director, and asked, "Why do you hate me? You've never even met me before!"

"I don't hate you," she laughed. "I scheduled you to speak now because *now* is when we need you. You see, *laughter is the catharsis that lets us keep on caring.*"

This book was inspired by her answer. It is full of ways patients and caregivers used the catharsis of humor to enhance life, share love or relieve stress in long-term care situations.

I share these examples in the hope that they will spark ideas that you can use in your situation and with the people you care for and about.

The human race has only one effective
weapon—and that is laughter.
—Mark Twain

A Prescription for Humor

There are times when, despite protestations to the contrary, laughter may not seem like the best medicine. You find yourself nursing someone through a long, possibly terminal, illness or providing home care for an elderly parent or spouse. Worse yet, perhaps you are the one with an illness in which the only happy ending may be a miracle or a death with dignity.

This does not mean there is no place for humor; it does mean that humor takes on a different role. If caregiver and patient can laugh together, both are encouraged to keep on caring. Humor that connects and touches both patient and caregiver heals by communicating such things as:

I know how you feel.
What you just said is funny.
You're so clever to be able to joke at this time.
What a great story you just told!
I love you, and I love our time together.

Physician and author Carl Hammerschlag says, "If you get in touch with feelings and you get in touch with others . . . you will be healed. You won't always be cured, but you will be healed."

Laughter may not be the best medicine to affect a cure, but it's often the most healing one available. The lows in long-term care can be very low, and the highs . . . well, they are not always that high—unless you exploit every drop of love and laughter in them. This book is intended to help you do just that!

Acknowledgments

I started this book as a chapter to an earlier one called "Creating a Legacy of Laughter." In talking to family members, friends, clients, and in at least one instance, my seatmate on an airplane, it quickly became apparent that nearly everyone has had some sort of experience with a loved one needing long-term care. As the stories came tumbling out, the project grew into the book you hold in your hand. Every story I heard was in some way incorporated into this book, albeit some more directly than others.

In addition to those named directly in the stories, I want to acknowledge Frank Adshead, Jeff Brandenburg, Vicky Kennedy, Marsha Lindsted, Margy Peterson, Maureen Roberts, Lee Schwab, and Michael and Gwen Spencer for sharing stories about their loved ones with me. I especially need to thank Marjori Munroe, Lily Dilig, Charmaine Cajucom, Rahel Hiyelu, Sharon Manies, and Jeff Jefferies. These folks embody caregiving, connective laughter and respect in ways I can only hope to emulate.

Special thanks also go to Lynn Durham for generously letting me print her poem,

"Death Asked Me to Dance;" to Christine Dubois, my oh-so-patient editor; and to all the friends I roped into sharing their feedback and proofreading skills with me, and by extension, dear reader, with you.

I am additionally indebted to all those, often unnamed, individuals who over the years shared a funny story or poignant example with me after one of my presentations. As a speaker, I've treasured those tales for the depth retelling them brought to my presentations. Now I find that, as an author, I treasure anew their ability to inspire my readers.

A special acknowledgment must also go to Elder Service Providers of Bellingham, Washington, for providing the impetus to write this book by agreeing to buy 50 of them sight unseen!

Dedication

This is dedicated to those who have, and those who will in the future, pursue the laughter and share the love in long-term care settings.

It is especially dedicated to my parents, Dick and Mary Schwab, my brother Richard, and niece Jennifer, who have all lived up close and personal with long-term care.

Table of Contents

Introduction

Laughing matters

Doc! You're depressing me!

The messages communicated in long-term or urgent care settings are often serious and laden with emotion: anger, frustration, embarrassment, hope, fear. Particularly in hospital settings, they often are communicated to and by strangers. Patients and caregivers are thrown together with no time to build a relationship and no expectation of a continuing relationship once the immediate health crisis is resolved.

Think about this. On one side of the relationship is a patient who is expected to trust the doctor or caregiver, accept his or her competency, allow this stranger to ask a variety of intimate questions and perform a series of painful and often embarrassing procedures—all of this, essentially on faith! On the other side is a physician or caregiver who is expected to share very little personal information. This is very odd. It does not fit the rules of a normal society.

That's why laughing matters. In these situations, perhaps more than in most, it is important to provide and encourage humor. Shared humor establishes rapport, something most patients desperately want with their caregivers. It helps reduce tension and, if the patient is creating it, by "making" the other person laugh, it decreases the power imbalance between the two individuals.

I learned this the hard way. In my early 40s, I forgot the most fundamental rule of horsemanship: Keep the horse on the bottom! The mare I was riding reared up and went over backwards on me. She walked away. I didn't.

I spent a month in the hospital with an initial prognosis that I would never walk again.

At the time I supervised a staff of 150. I was the boss. One of the most threatening things for me during my hospital stay was that I no longer owned my own functions. Suddenly the basic things I did for myself were taken away: eating, dressing, going to the bathroom.

I made jokes, in part to remove some of the tension and embarrassment, but also to regain a sense of control. It was my way of letting my caregivers know that my brain was still functioning even if my body wasn't.

Make humor a window of opportunity— not a pane!

Humor exchanged between patient and caregiver can be a little tricky—especially if they don't know each other well. Here are a few clues on how to introduce it.

Patient humor: The difficulty with using humor when you are sick or old (i.e. older than the caregiver) is that a lot of the medical staff will not be expecting it. If you don't present your humor broadly, or lead folks up to it in obvious ways, you run the risk of them thinking that your medication needs to be adjusted or that you are simply going gaga!

The rule is to start with the safe stuff—for example, the questions listed under "Make humor easy for yourself" on page 8 of this book. Be sure to allow a twinkle to come into your eye and a smile to your lips as clues that what you are saying has a humorous kick to it.

Caregiver humor: LAUGH. So you heard the joke before, laugh anyway. The laughter is for the patient's sake, not the joke's. If you hear a particular joke a lot, spend the time to create a funny, reassuring response. Here's why.

At age 72, Richard was an avid tennis player and cyclist. To cover his concern about how a second hernia operation might affect his athletic ability, he tried joking that the doctor "should just put in a zipper."

With a stern look, his doctor snapped, "I don't do that!"

Nice, huh? In one sentence, the physician managed to sound like a jerk and made his patient feel like a fool. He could have just as easily said, "Sorry, Richard, my work is so good I don't leave a scar big enough for a zipper!" THAT sentence would have honored his patient's sense of humor and reassured him that he was in good hands.

Many caregivers are legitimately worried about laughing at something a patient means seriously. Navy nurse Maureen Roberts told me of having patients who really *were* worried that they had contacted "Spinal Moaning Jesus" (when they meant Spinal Meningitis) or that they might be sent to the "Insensitive Care Unit" (confused with the Intensive Care Unit).

Rather than offering an officious correction, Maureen's ready laugh reassures them and implies they actually said something clever.

When introducing humor to a patient situation, the above rule about starting with the "safe stuff" applies. Bolder humor often works better if 1) a relationship has already been established, and 2) a misstatement or clever line is attributed to a hypothetical patient. For example, say something like, "I had a patient awhile ago with an amputation who insisted that the one positive outcome was that he could run for public office. He figured, of all the candidates, he'd have the best 'stump speech!' "

The bottom line is that, as beauty is in the eye of the beholder, humor is in the funny bone of the receiver. Not all of your humor will connect, but chances are your intention to reach out in a caring, personal way will. In the end, it's the strength of that caring connection, not the size of the laugh, that heals.

Get your point across with humor.

Keep Your Spirits up the Easy Way

Tap into the humor around you

Positive, humorous people make life worth living and work worth doing well. Because laughing together implies similar experiences, perspectives and values, shared humor can forge a powerful bond between patient and caregiver.

The first six ideas below are ways that relative strangers, as patient and caregiver often are, can connect with humor. Ideas seven through 10 are selfishly just for you—but doing them will make the folks around you happier to be around you!

NOTE: All 10 ideas work whether or not someone sick is involved. They're included because they are easy to do. If you are a patient, or if you are caring for someone who is, something *easy* to do should be music to your ears!

1. Create playful people

Create an atmosphere that encourages the playful, inventive, supportive side of friends, caregivers, neighbors and everyone else in your life to come forth. They'll create the humor for you. Laugh at their jokes and antics. Encourage them to share their mirth at meetings, meals and other meaningful moments. It is as important to respond to the humor in others as it is to create that humor in the first place. Allowing someone to "make you laugh" is a wonderful gift you can give another person, and at the same time, they will brighten up your day.

2. Make humor easy for yourself

Absolutely the easiest way to get more humor in your life is to ask others to tell you something funny. Ask the folks around you a simple question such as: "What funny thing happened to you today?" or "Tell me about the most amazing patient you ever had." If you are the patient, refuse to allow a caregiver to do a procedure until they tell you something funny. It's a great way to exert a little authority!

To really get to know someone, ask a leading question such as:

Who makes you laugh more than anyone?

What was your favorite toy as a child?

What was your first car like?

What is the strangest or funniest thing you've ever done for money?

Questions like the above are as fun to answer as the answers are fun to hear, and they will quickly take a new relationship to a deeper, more personal level.

3. Share good gossip

Make a daily
habit of sharing
at least three
good things that
happened to
someone else. It
could be an
award they won,
or a funny story
they told you

about their children, or the fact that they have
beautiful flowers in their yard, or that their team
won the softball game. Do this for a month and
see what a difference it makes to the atmosphere
around you.

4. Give three compliments

A variation of this is to give three genuine
compliments a day to total strangers. Again,
check how you feel after a month. My bet is
you'll feel stronger and more in control, knowing
you have the power to light up someone's life.

5. Create humor from your life

Take events that really happened to you and
make them into funny stories. Each of us has lots
of personal anecdotes stored away that can bring
smiles and laughter to friends, drive important

points home to caregivers, and create memories for loved ones. When our own morale is drooping, retelling these stories can be a reminder of our ability to survive difficult situations. An added bonus is that if you tell funny stories about things that really happened, you will never have trouble remembering the punch line!

For example, in the horseback riding accident I mentioned earlier, I showed up in the emergency room with a broken back and assorted other injuries. I wasn't thinking about anything except how much it hurt. Luckily, I had caregivers who provided the humor to help me get some perspective on my situation. It started with the surgeon who solemnly apologized that he couldn't give me a bikini cut because he needed to do exploratory surgery to find out why I was bleeding internally. He paused for dramatic effect and then concluded that he personally felt that a vertical cut was more slimming! (He was right, I'm still proud of my 11-inch racing stripe!)

6. Make a 'Good Stuff List'

For one month—or however long it takes you to establish the mental habit—make a daily list of the good things that happen. If you can't find any good things, lower your standards! Remember, not all of us can win the lottery or end world hunger. We can, however, celebrate finding an empty parking place, seeing a beautiful sunset, or even passing a blood test. The goal of a Good Stuff List is quantity: How many good, funny, positive things can you find? The phrase to remember is, "People who are easy to please, get pleased a lot."

Allow yourself to be easily pleased.

7. Review the good stuff in your life

Create your list in a notebook or diary so that it will be easy to review past days, weeks and months. When you are feeling depressed, re-read your list. If you are REALLY feeling down, add something good to the list. Review your "Good Stuff List" before you go to bed each night—it will put a smile on your sleeping face!

8. 'Hold' the jokes

Does being "on hold" get to you? Keep a joke book by your phone and only allow yourself to read it while you wait on hold. It can speed the time to the point that you will actually be disappointed when the person you are waiting for comes on the line.

9. Be well read

If you keep up with current events and with issues in your field, it will be easy for you to insert spontaneous remarks or a recent humorous quote into conversations. In addition to bringing humor to the situation, funny comments and jokes about current events show off your knowledge and insight. Most of us could benefit from having a reputation as a knowledgeable, insightful humorist.

10. Don't forget the two major rules of humor

As you develop your stories and anecdotes, remember the two most important rules of humor:

1. Anything worth telling is worth exaggerating.

2. Never let the truth get in the way of a good story!

When Life Freezes Over— Ice Skate!

Use the safest, most affordable, medicine around!

Health care advice seems to fall into two camps: the "Making Sacrifices" camp and the "Quick Fix" camp. The former consists of doing all those "It's good for you" things that many of us are not normally inclined to do: exercise, keep our temper, eat right, take certain medications regularly, etc.

Perhaps you have seen the bumper sticker:

> I didn't fight my way to the top of the food chain to be a vegetarian!

That pretty much sums up my feelings. I mean, there you are, on top of the old food chain, and you look over and what do you see dominating that nutritional pyramid? Lentils! To someone raised Catholic, as I was, anything with the word "lent" in it already sounds like a sacrifice!

Then there is the "Quick Fix" camp, which consists of doing things many of us *are* inclined to do: take a magic pill, eat dark chocolate, sniff the musk from the wild boar of some remote South Seas island. My personal favorite is the Seaweed Weight Loss Soap where "The lather penetrates the skin to break up fat globules as you wash!" (Trust me, it doesn't.)

The downside of this camp is that many of us can't help feeling that we are being ripped off; few, if any, of us get well; and, except for those of us eating chocolate, most of us don't feel any better.

So what's a body to do?

Laugh it off! Really!

One of the best things about humor is that it fits into both camps. It's "good for us," and, at the same time, it's something most of us *are* inclined to do.

There is documentation aplenty about the psychological advantages of wit and humor. Even a casual observer can notice how the mental processes involved in creating humor increase creative problem-solving abilities, provide a sense of perspective that reduces stress, and instill an air of competence on the humorist.

As for the physiological benefits of hearty laughter, let me simply cite some of the earliest findings by Dr. Bill Fry, a psychiatrist at Stanford Medical School. Dr. Fry studied the physiological benefits of laughter for more than 40 years. Here is what he found accompanies a hearty laugh:

1. The heart and blood circulation rates soar, imitating the effects of an aerobic workout. While sick people are not big on aerobics, most would happily add a few guffaws to their day.

2. Muscles vibrate, providing an internal massage that breaks up tension, stimulates the digestive system, and helps fight gastro-intestinal track problems. Hello, bedridden folks? We are talking natural laxative here!

3. The deep respiration that accompanies laughter increases oxygen in the blood. By some measures, a laughing person takes in six times more oxygen than someone who is simply talking. By oxygenating muscles, laughter helps reduce cramping and tension.

4. After the laughter subsides, the pulse rate drops below normal, promoting relaxation.

In Norman Cousins' seminal book, "Anatomy of an Illness" (1979), he notes that 15 minutes of hearty laughter produced three hours of deep sleep.

I don't want to oversell the case for humor and healing. Humor is best viewed as something that, in concert with other practices, augments and improves the situation.

Think, if you will, of humor as a vitamin. Here are some ways patients and caregivers alike have found to supplement each other's daily minimum requirements of "Vitamin H."

1. Don't be paralyzed by your attitude

Eighty-nine-year-old Margaretta Boucher is consistently upbeat and full of life despite braces on both legs and one arm withered from polio. When asked the secret to her remarkable attitude, Margaretta explained, "My mother died when I was 5 years old, and I got polio the next year.

Then, when I was a teen, I went to the hospital with pneumonia. One day a nurse sat down and had a heart-to-heart talk with me. She said, 'You are going to have polio the rest of your life. You can be cranky and spend the rest of your life with polio and no friends, or you can be cheerful and spend the rest of your life with polio and friends. It's your decision.' I never forgot that."

And, I would add, she has lots of friends to confirm the choice she made!

2. Grow where you are planted

I interviewed Margaretta in her home, where she lives alone. She regaled me with stories of how the delivery man from Albertson's grocery store sat on the floor and rearranged her wine cabinet for her, how her son-in-law invented an electric lift to allow her to get up from the floor if she fell when no one was around, and how her grandson *wanted* to live in her mother-in-law apartment, just to hang out with her. Most importantly, she told me how she learned the secret of letting others get involved in her life.

"One day my daughter and I bought some plants and brought them back to my house. She wanted to repot them for me before she went home. I made a fuss because I wanted to think about which pots I'd put them in and how I would mix the plants in each pot.

"Suddenly she started crying and insisted, 'I

just can't do this. Nothing I do for you is ever right! I can't come here anymore!'

"Right there and then I realized that I had to let go—and that as my disability progressed, I would have to let go even more. Now I never complain when someone does something for me—even if it isn't done the way I would do it, at least it's done!"

3. Create good from bad

She's Doin' Great!

Take a not-so-funny event and explore the humor in it. For example, Gary Y. drives a para-transit bus in Yakima, Wash. When his wife got cancer, he shaved his head to support her. To stem the solicitous comments from his passengers— who, for the most part, only see the back of his head—Gary writes updates and other messages on his bald pate.

4. Have fun with limericks

Archie Drake, an 81-year-old bass baritone who sang with the Seattle Opera for 39 seasons, could find humor—and write a limerick—about darn near anything. He wrote the following one about a sigmoidoscopy:

One would think there could be nothing drearier
Than peering up one's own posterior.
But, my word, what you see
On full-color TV!
Seems I have quite a pretty interior!

5. Celebrate obscure holidays

When you are sick, it can be difficult to find things to celebrate, and national holidays don't necessarily show up at appropriate times.

Let me suggest that you look to obscure holidays when you need a real break or celebration. There is one practically every day of the year begging to be noticed. Valuable opportunities such as Penguin Awareness Day (Jan. 20), Awkward Moments Day (March 18), Patt Schwab's Birthday Day (April 25), Eat What You Want Day (May 11), Sneak a Zucchini Night (Aug. 8), Boost Your Brain Day (Oct. 18), and even Shallow Person's Week (second week in November), should not go uncelebrated!

Here is a day for each month, just to get you started. Feel free to interpret them any way you want—you are the one celebrating, so you are the one in charge! In fact, create holidays from whatever inspires you: family history, TV shows or clean laundry.

Jan. 8	Bubble Bath Day
Feb. 15	National Gum Drop Day
March 19	Wellderly Day *(for elders who don't act their age)*
April 12	Walk On Your Wild Side Day
May 28	The Great American Grump Out
June 23	Let It Go Day
July 3	Compliment Your Mirror On Its Owner Day
Aug. 6	International Forgiveness Day
Sept. 9	Thank the Wonderful Weirdoes Day
Oct. 4	Toot Your Flute Day
Nov. 30	Call in Well Day
Dec. 11	Do What You Want Day

6. Create a humor book

It's tough for kids to visit sick adults. Here's an idea, adapted from Joel Goodman, to help a child (of any age) start creating a legacy of laughter.

Ask your child or grandchild to review all the funny or clever things that he or she saw in the past few days. When the two of you settle on the funniest, write the incident in a journal and let the child draw a picture to illustrate the event. In addition to sharing some wonderful time together and creating a volume that will be treasured for decades to come, you will also be encouraging your child to start looking for the funny, silly, creative, positive things in life.

7. Encourage tacky tourism

Hold a contest to see who can send you the best "tacky tourist" postcard or gift from their travels. (My personal favorite was the tequila lollipop with a worm inside.) Decorate the sick room with them. A wall full of silly, inventive cards will cheer up all who enter, provide upbeat interesting conversation starters and remind you of how clever and thoughtful your friends are.

8. Invent good fortune

Print up a series of good fortunes, funny sayings, health tips or inside jokes. Take them to a fortune cookie factory or to a website like www. Fancyfortunecookies.com and ask them to insert them for you. Then give them to your ailing friend before a particularly nasty procedure, like a chemo treatment. It's a light-hearted way to show that good fortune can come out of bad circumstances.

9. Think funny

Thinking funny about a problem often sparks creative solutions.

When I was in the hospital with my broken back, my rehab group was required to make nightly endurance treks around the floor.

These were unbelievably strenuous for a group as pathetic as we were: two stroke patients, a guy with an aneurysm, another (the only one who could walk unassisted) with an IV to flush out a kidney stone, and me. Picture us shepherded by a somber nurse who periodically rushed into our lineup to keep one of us from tipping over.

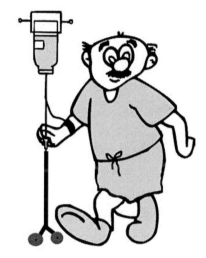

One night someone (I wish I could say it was me) announced, "If we have to be in these %$^&*!! parades, let's do them right!" He then produced Groucho glasses, hats, balloons, kazoos, and assorted other accoutrements for us to use. Instantly the dynamics changed! That night the length of our walk extended by almost 25 percent, other patients wanted to get in on the fun, and our somber nurse was laughing so hard we had to prop her up!

From then on we held nightly "Endurance Parades," which we are convinced sped our recovery.

10. Notice 'puns in nature'

When kids are young, they like puns because the word play helps them get over the tension of not always knowing the right word. The first such pun I remember seeing was on a fruit stand in front of a San Francisco hospital. As my mother cheerfully pointed out "Patty, that's the hospital where you were born!" all I could see was the sign saying, "Juicy Navels for Sale!"

The doctors were selling bellybuttons on the street! And they were juicy! For a second grader, that was funny.

If you find yourself in a new environment, be on the lookout for "Puns in Nature." They can often be found by taking signs literally. One of my favorites was sighted outside a Seattle hospital. It directed patrons to:

One day when I was in the hospital rehab wing, the man in the next room, a head injury patient, came wheeling in begging me to hide him. "Why?" I asked. "What did you do?"

"Well," he said, "I only did what the sign said, and now the nurse is mad at me!"

"And the sign said . . . what?"

"Wet floor!" he replied with a grin.

11. Let the son shine in

The last story in this book is about Marilyn Brandenburg's funeral. When I asked her son, Jeff, if I could include it, his response was, "Mom was an inspiration to everybody while she was here—no reason to change the pattern now that she isn't." (As someone who knew Marilyn, that was the answer I had hoped for.)

Jeff also shared a moment from the beginning of Marilyn's illness that showed the kind of resilience she (and he) brought to the entire ordeal.

"The doctor had just given us the diagnosis: lung cancer that had spread to her liver, hip, and brain. He left the room to give us a minute to think about treatment, and we sat quietly. Then Mom said to me, 'Jeff, I'm sure glad you're here. I don't think I could remember all the details he just told us.'

"With a straight and somber face, I replied, 'Well, that's because you have tumors in your head!'

"Mom started howling with laughter, as the doctor walked back into the room. The look on his face made us both bust up all over again."

The laughter gave them both a feeling of triumph over an unbearably painful situation. Jeff revealed that one of his self-assigned jobs became trying to keep things as light as possible.

12. Express your hang-ups

Create "Patient Protection Door Hangers" for yourself (or for your sick friends). These are door hangers that acknowledge that sick people have a range of feelings, some of which are not so cheerful. Here are some that have been well received by my circle of sick pals:

- COME IN ONLY if you have a smile, a kind word, or a great joke!
- NAP TIME! Get your book and come on in.
- I DON'T WANT TO BE CHEERED UP! (Maybe later, but not now, OK!!)

13. Recycle humor

Print up a series of jokes or one-liners on strips of paper, or gather up all those Joke-a-Day calendar pages and fold or crumple them up. Put them in a Humor Prescription Jar on a handy table and encourage people to take one as needed for a low calorie pick-me-up.

Note: "Vitamin H" is great medicine for folks with an Irony Deficiency!

14. It's a win/win situation

Rahel Hiyelu is putting herself through nursing school working as a caregiver in an assisted living facility at night and doing home care during the afternoon. When I asked how she could maintain such a rigorous schedule, she explained:

"I know I am helping people when I do the physical things like feeding, bathing, toileting or dressing them. But the truth is that those things just prolong life. What I like most about this work is how I can make a difference in the *quality* of someone's life, simply by listening to them.

"It can be very lonely in an assisted living facility if you have no friends or family visiting you. People want to connect with others. They want to be remembered, to leave, if nothing else, some sort of oral legacy.

"When I laugh at their jokes and respond to their stories, it's not just to be kind. I win, too. I honestly enjoy the stories they tell me about their children or the jobs they had or what they did when they were young. Some residents have even given me good advice—advice I actually used!"

15. 'Can you hear me now?' is not just for cell phone users

Rahel also told me how she handled Alise, a resident who entered the assisted living facility dining room like Queen Elisabeth—the ship, not

the individual. At each meal, she would take her walker into the most congested part of the room, insisting that everyone move aside to allow her passage. Her apparent inability to hear any explanations, complaints, or general grumbling was blamed on a mysterious, recurring meltdown of her hearing aid.

In truth, Alise played fast and loose with that hearing aid. When the staff gave her choices, her hearing magically improved. For example, at bedtime, Rahel would ask, "Alise, can you hear me? It's time for bed." Alise would insist she couldn't hear her until Rahel said, "OK, just push your call button when you decide you want to go to bed." As she started to leave, inevitably—and with complete understanding—Alise would say, "Yes, I want to go to bed now."

16. Let someone reach out to you

Helping hands can come from lots of places. Keep your eyes open for them, and be quick with an acknowledgement and a shared laugh.

Mary D.'s husband has advanced MS. Late for

a meeting, she was pushing him in his wheelchair swiftly across a parking lot. The chair hit a crack, tossing him unceremoniously onto the pavement.

Two men rushed over, and without even really looking at Mary, picked up her husband and settled him back in his wheelchair. In a voice full of mock seriousness, one of them said to him, "I don't know about you, but if it was me, I'd get a new driver!"

17. Youth deficiency

At 86, Susan had never been sick in her life. After her annual physical, her doctor pronounced that all she was suffering from was "Youth Deficiency!"

Since he wouldn't prescribe a youth for her, Susan has concluded that she needs to find one on her own. From the look in her eye when she announced this to me, I'd say any guy under 80 better look out!

18. What to do with a platitude?

My father was attending a funeral for his friend Hal and found himself making small talk with the deceased's grandson. The younger man opined, "I'm sure going to miss Grandpa, but he lived a long, full, rich life, and it was time for him to go."

"I guess so," said my dad, "but where does that leave me? I'm eight years older than Hal was!"

19. Shower yourself with tropical fantasies

We live in a hurried world and even being sick doesn't always slow it down. That's when it's time to remember a lesson I learned from a man in Spokane, Washington. He has a large shower with a seat in it. Each morning, after finishing his shower, he leaves the water running while he sits on the seat and drinks a big glass of fresh-squeezed orange juice. He told me, "An observer might think I'm in a shower stall in Spokane, but, at least for a minute or two, I *know* I'm on a holiday in the tropics!"

20. R-E-S-P-E-C-T! Find out what it means to me!

Genet Aklilu is a home care worker who has to deal with lots of different personalities, family settings, and personal care demands. Needless to say, she doesn't always work in a happy, upbeat atmosphere.

I doubt that Genet has heard of Aretha Franklin's hit, but she certainly knows how to show respect for her patients.

She told me, "In my native Ethiopia, we have a lot of respect for old people—in fact I was raised by my grandfather—so it comes naturally for me to be respectful, even if the patient isn't."

21. It's Greek to me

With a cheerful laugh, Genet told me about a patient who refused to wear his hearing aids and kept complaining about her accent.

"I've been in the USA over 12 years and no other patients complained about my having an accent. I tried talking slower. I tried talking louder, but I think he just wanted to complain. He kept saying 'I don't understand you. Everything you say is Greek to me!'

"Since my job depends on my being nice, I just smiled . . . and reminded myself that he only knew one language, while I speak three—and one of mine actually is Greek!"

22. Accent the positive

Genet told me about one old man who was just plain mean. He complained about everything—right down to the length of the spaghetti Meals on Wheels brought him! "All the caregivers hated to go to his house. We'd silently repeat, 'Thank heavens it's only a three-hour shift!'

"One time his complaints got so outrageous I started laughing. Startled, he looked at me and then he started laughing too. 'I guess it is pretty silly, after all,' he said. We got along much better after that."

23. Keep your balance with humor

Molly, a home care nurse, told me about a mishap transferring a large male patient. His feet went out from under him, and the two of them hit the floor, with her on the bottom. As she struggled to get out from under him, he jokingly shouted, "Help! I've fallen! And *you* can't get up!"

That caused them both to laugh so hard they couldn't begin to get up for another five minutes!

24. Ask yourself: What would Lawrence Welk do?

Approach life from a Lawrence Welk perspective. Last summer, as in many summers before, the 5 p.m. traffic on Seattle's I-520 bridge was oozing along at 2-3 m.p.h. What made last summer different was the man holding a Bubble Bear out his car window. As the bubbles floated in the still air, nearby drivers relaxed, smiled and even pointed out especially big bubbles to one another.

Think of where you could add bubbles to lighten someone's day, or to provide a bit of respiratory exercise for some tired lungs.

Act Eccentric!

Make age and infirmity work to your advantage

I have always believed that you should start acting eccentric when you are young so that people won't think you're getting gaga when you get old. If you are already a bit "long in the tooth," and you haven't established any obvious eccentricities, by all means get started! The real joy of getting older is that you can get away with more. Here are some wonderful examples of older folks having a bit of fun.

1. Share an elevating experience

Have you noticed that when you are in an elevator no one talks, they all face front and stare in fascination at the floor numbers going by? Use the power of eccentricity to change this.

Face the other people and say, "Hi there!" like they are old friends or lost lovers! Ask them how their children are or if they like their new house or if they've decided whom to vote for yet. If they say they have no children or have lived in their current house for 10 years, simply launch into a new topic.

Your goal is to give them something to talk about later. The game only ends when one of you reaches your floor—though you may find that their floor comes up sooner than the one they initially pushed!

2. Use your walker as a weapon

You know how, as you head for a supermarket line, there is a tacit agreement to yield to the individual who started toward the line first? Somehow this rule seems not to apply when that "first" person is using a walker. Suddenly it becomes a race going to the swiftest instead of a courtesy granted to the more observant.

Vicky has been using a walker long enough to get sick and tired of this behavior. When someone zips in front of her in line, she plants the cutting edge of her walker so it just scrapes the back of their ankle. When they whirl around and complain, she apologizes profusely and says, "I'm so sorry, I didn't see you cut in front of me!"

3. Create your own Boy Scout

Ida, a woman, in her 80s, navigates around San Francisco by bus. If her travels take her through rush hour, she frequently finds herself standing on a crowded bus. She did, that is, until she decided to stop waiting for a courteous Boy Scout and create her own. Now she hands her cane to the nearest able-bodied seated person, smiles sweetly and asks: "Would you mind holding this so that I can hold on with both hands?" She told me that it is a rare person who doesn't offer her a seat.

4. Don't mess with old folks

At 104, Ona was the oldest person in her nursing home. She was mentally quite sharp, but described herself as "about as agile as your average 104-year-old."

What she hated most was being put on display every time the nursing home wanted to show off to the local newspaper or television station or promote itself to prospective residents.

One day she had had enough.

The nursing home director introduced her to a reporter from the big city daily and then asked, "Ona, who is president of the United States?" Ona looked at the reporter, gave him a wicked smile, and defiantly answered, "Abraham Lincoln!"

5. Gotcha!

When Jeff J. was a graduate student in geriatric social work, he had a counseling assignment to "get to know someone" in a local senior center.

Jeff dutifully introduced himself to an elderly woman and explained that, as a grad student in geriatric counseling, he was very knowledgeable about the field, and asked if there was anything with which he could help her.

She thought for a few minutes while Jeff adopted his best counseling demeanor. Finally, she looked at him and said, "A few months ago I ordered these blinds from Penney's, and I don't have anyone to put them up!"

Jeff's mind did a double back flip, but luckily he landed on his feet—lightly. "Let's go," he smiled. "Do you have a screwdriver?"

6. Gotcha again!

A few years later, Jeff J. was working in a nursing home and found himself in a debate with several other young staff trying to determine at what age does sex cease to be important.

Jeff had become friends with an 85-year-old woman in the facility and decided to put an end to the discussion once and for all by asking her, "When do people stop thinking about sex?"

She chuckled and said, "Honey, I'm afraid you'll have to ask someone older than I am!"

7. A race to the finish

Dr. Dennis Dennis told me about the many fun things his mom, Valeri, did to keep folks around her on their toes. (Actually, any woman who names her son Dennis Dennis is someone to watch out for!)

He said, "My mother had a great sense of humor. She frequently joked about her 'wooden leg,' the result of a tragic childhood accident. She managed to find humor in it, despite the blatant discrimination she endured at the hands of employers and various institutions. Unfortunately, ADA came too late to benefit her.

"I suspect her ability to laugh at adversity helped her ward off lung cancer for 60 years until it finally got her. Following her diagnosis, humor made her last months fun and meaningful until the very end."

The last seven to eight years of her life Valeri rode everywhere in an Electric Mobility 'Scooter.' She always wore a bicycle helmet, and in cooler weather a black leather jacket. Appropriately, her e-mail address was RoadhogRascal@aol.com. Ten weeks before she died, at age 81, she sent Dennis this e-mail:

> "We went to K Mart yesterday, I rode
> my Scooter. Oh, I had a RACE
> w/a woman there, & I WON !!"

8. A rolling stone gathers no moss

"My mother loved games," Dennis told me, "and was a competitive person until the end. Two months before the e-mail notifying me of her scooter race victory, she won our last Scrabble game against my sister, my daughter and myself."

For years Valeri Dennis' outgoing voice message excitedly proclaimed: "A rolling stone gathers no moss—so I'm outa here!" Her message was immediately followed by an accelerating Harley Davidson sound she had dubbed in from an official H-D audio beer mug. Then a cheery, "Don't forget to leave a message!"

The recording became such a trademark that her family played it at her funeral!

9. You can always sit in a raft when you get old

Pat and her boyfriend, Bruster, were both 79 years old. They went on annual cross country ski trips all over the world, usually with people 25 to 30 years younger than they were.

My friend Evelyn Clark met them when they came to the Northwest for some summertime recreation. After a week of hiking around Mount Rainier and another of llama backpacking in the Cascade Mountains, they were having dinner with Evelyn and the mutual friends who had lured them to the West Coast.

As they planned their next adventure, their host, knowing that rafting the Colorado River was high on their "To Do List," asked them, "Do you want to do the Colorado next year or do you want to go on another llama backpacking trip?"

"I want to go backpacking," said Pat without any hesitation. "I can always sit in a raft when I get old."

Evelyn, at the time dreading an upcoming 40th birthday, admits to having done a quick reassessment of her concept of old age!

Indulge your eccentricities. If not now, when?

The Fowl Side of Illness

Develop rubber chicken flexibility

If you are the caregiver, your anger, crabbiness, pain or frustration does not benefit your patient or loved one—nor, for that matter the other caregivers who may be with you.

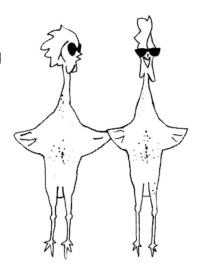

If you are the patient, your anger, crabbiness, pain or frustration does not benefit the people you need most at this annoying juncture in your life—nor does it encourage them to extend themselves when you need an extra bit of attention.

Yet these feelings are entirely natural in times of stress and illness. You need to find an outlet for your feelings that does not unduly impact on others.

This is the perfect time to . . .

Find a fowl weather friend

Rubber chickens work. I don't know why, they just do. There is something about a rubber chicken that courts all of life's trials and helps resolve them. They are the ultimate Om-birds-man.

Perhaps it's their flexibility. They don't care if you dress them up or bang them on a table to vent frustration. If you're happy, they're happy. If you're not happy, they're happy to do whatever it takes to make you happy again.

Get one.
Put sunglasses on it so it looks cool.
It will give you something to crow about.

1. Get a rubber chicken

When you find you are losing your perspective, take out your chicken and look at it. Allow it to remind you that emotionally upset people are lousy problem solvers, and that you need to lighten up in order to attack your problem creatively.

If this doesn't work, hang the rubber chicken in your doorway or place it prominently in your room to let people know you are having a fowl day!

2. Drive with a rubber chicken

Keep a rubber chicken in the front seat of the car. Next time someone cuts you off in traffic, instead of getting angry, roll down your window and wave your chicken at him! It will confuse him, help you keep your sense of humor, and it's one way of "flipping someone the bird" that you can do in front of the kids!

3. Talk to your rubber chicken

Become a "Break Glass in Emergency" rubber chicken user. Keep one in a nearby drawer. Use it when you really need to change your mood, clear your brain of some jerk, or get a new perspective on a problem. Describe your frustration in detail to your chicken—they are great listeners. Plus, the mere thought that you are actually *talking* to a rubber chicken should jolt you out of your stuck place!

4. Use an emergency rubber chicken

There may be a stressor so great that you will need to go public with your chicken, but that still doesn't mean losing your dignity. Imagine coming home to a broken dishwasher that has poured water all over your hardwood floor in sufficient quantity that it has also ruined your dining room rug.

The colorful, expressive language that leaps to your throat cannot be uttered because the kids, or some friends who think highly of you, are present. Somehow dignity must be retained. This is not easy to do UNLESS you have your rubber chicken.

You simply take it out, bang it severely on the counter for 1 to 2 minutes until your equilibrium is restored—or the silliness of the situation becomes clear. Then put your chicken away and call the repair folks.

5. Downsize your rubber chicken

Keep a rubber chicken at hand and under wraps by downsizing it. Get a rubber chicken key chain, or one of a variety of palm-size rubber chickens currently in novelty stores. Hide it in a pocket or under a blanket and use it as you would a worry stone or stress ball.

Want to get in good with a hard-working nurse, caregiver, receptionist or Access driver? Give them a pocket rubber chicken as a thank-you / cheer-up/I-appreciate-you gift. They only cost about 50 cents, but, wow, do they light up the recipient's face!

6. Upgrade to a code yellow rubber chicken

The truth is, not all emergencies are equal. There are the serious code blues and reds, which are the responsibility of the medical crowd. Then there are a patient's own special "code yellows." These are called when you have answered the same #%$#^& question a zillion times; when it hurts and you know nothing can be done about it; when you are desperate to be turned over or given fresh water; or when, no matter what your age, you want your mommy!

The Code Yellow Rubber Chicken is a

screecher. You just give him a squeeze, and he lets loose with an ear piercing squawk that expresses your frustration better than you ever dreamed.

If you want to provide a special surprise for your caregiver, roll over on your chicken. It will push the air out of him, and he will lie quietly in place. That is, until that tech comes in to roll you over for a shot or a blood draw. Then, BOY HOWDY, does your chicken tell them fast how you dislike that procedure!

Squaaaawk!!

P.S.—If you aren't ambulatory, request a rubber chicken from a friend. It's the perfect assignment for the friend who's always saying, "Can I bring you something?"

What! Me Worry?

Reduce stress with humor

Whenever I would complain that the world wasn't fair, my grandma would agree. She'd say, "Of course the world isn't fair. It's not even logical. If the world were a logical place, men would ride sidesaddle!"

My grandma's gone now, but her wisdom lingers. The next time you worry about how the kids are doing in school, or how you're going to make the mortgage payment, or whether or not they will find a cure for your disease in time, think about using a little humor. Humor doesn't belittle a problem, it helps put it into perspective.

Here are some easy ways to try it out.

1. Set a worry time

The trouble with worrying is that it doesn't solve anything, and too much worrying gets in the way of problem solving and of healing. Use a little humor to get perspective on your worries.

Schedule 15 minutes each day to worry. (After lunch is good because it's a notoriously unproductive time anyway.) When worrisome things come up at other times, jot them down and save them for your "Worry Time."

When your "Worry Time" comes up, make a chart listing the things you are worried about in one column. Then make three more columns as follows:

Worry	Things I can control	Things I can affect through others	Things I cannot control
Worry #1			
Worry #3			
Worry #3			

If your worry fits into column one or two and you can take action on it, take it—or schedule it to be taken. You will be surprised, however, how few items fit into an action category! If you have no control over an item, let it go.

If you don't finish worrying in 15 minutes, leave the rest of the items for the next day—you may even want to add an item indicating that you are worried about not fitting all your worries into the allotted time!

2. Play the blame game

Sometimes we just need someone to blame. It may be our own fault or no one's fault, but that doesn't stem the need to shift responsibility.

Post a sign saying: The person to blame for everything wrong this week is: _____! Each week a different family member, friend or caregiver gets to be "the Person." Heck, why stop there? Pick politicians, plumbers, ex-true loves, whomever you want to blame—for anything! The sign ends fault-finding by focusing on how silly —and arbitrary—blaming people is.

3. Bond together in tense times

Develop a family chant, song or whine to see you through tough times. They're fun to make up, and repeating them together builds a supportive bond that can last well beyond an illness.

4. Read between the parallel bars

When I was learning to walk after breaking my back, my physical therapist, Chris Hellwich, used humor to encourage me. To build my endurance, she would make me stand in the parallel bars. For someone like me, with little feeling or muscle control from the waist down, this wasn't easy.

To keep me standing, Chris would distract me with her oral interpretations of humorous stories, Dave Barry columns, and the like. The minute I stopped standing, she stopped reading. Talk about positive reinforcement! I can think of many a day when, although exhausted, my standing was extended by my desire to hear the end of a story.

5. Make 'helpful' lists

Putting your complaints or insights into a list can be a great way to let go of problems and crank up your brain for creative thinking. And, if you post your lists on the wall or on-line, others can join in the fun.

Good Reasons to Get Old

1. beats alternative
2. get to act eccentric
3. know who friends are
4. can claim wisdom
5. can get away with stuff

Submit your most outrageous list as an article to a magazine or as a Top 10 List to Letterman. Who knows? If you have yet to achieve your 15 minutes of fame, this might be your chance!

Here are some ideas to get you started.

15 Sure Fire Ways to Get a Doctor's Attention
10 Best Reasons for Getting Old
8 New Uses for Ensure
Depends vs. Thongs—You Decide!

Here's a sample list, compiled by friends and borrowed from the Internet, of why you should always choose a general anesthesia—no matter what the doctor says.

12 Things You Don't Want to Hear in Surgery:

1. Oops!
2. Has anyone seen my watch?
3. Hurry, I don't want to miss "American Idol."
4. Hold on. If this is his spleen, what's that?
5. Hand me that . . . uh . . . that uh . . . thingy.
6. You mean he wasn't in for a sex change!
7. Rats! There go the lights again.
8. Everybody stand back! I lost my contact lens!
9. Well folks, this will be an experiment for us.
10. What do you mean, she's not insured?
11. What do you mean, "You want a divorce?"
12. Since it's the first time anyone has ever tried this procedure, win, lose, or draw, this patient is going to be famous!

6. Create a blog—or read one

If you get a really good list, post it on a blog so others can enjoy it—and even add to it. Better yet, check out the blogs of other people fighting the fight you are fighting. They can commiserate, hook you up with resources, share solutions that worked for them and, just possibly, provide you with a few chuckles and a new support group.

7. Indulge in art with angst

Having trouble with a specific individual? Draw a picture of him or her. (This is a great exercise if you are a lousy artist because you want a lousy picture.) Label it with the person's name and an adjective (Compulsive Carl, Bumbling Betty, etc.) and put it in your pocket, under your pillow (or, if you really have issues, under your bedpan). The next time you have to deal with the person, take the paper in your hand and crumple it, twist it around a bit. In some weird way, this little activity will help you take back some of the power you let them have over how you feel. The big plus is that it leaves your mind free to cope with whatever the real problem is.

8. Extract healthy vengeance

Trying to cope with a tough situation? Make a salad from scratch. This is a particularly effective stress reducer if you *name* the vegetables before you cut them up! If they won't let you have sharp implements, tear the vegetables up with your bare hands. Season your creation with appropriate guttural sounds.

9. Walk on the bad guys

Still having trouble? Get the biggest, fattest marker pen you can find and write the bad guys' names on the bottom of your shoe. Practice walking on them for a few days! If nothing else, this technique can encourage a patient to get ambulatory in a hurry!

10. Make a 'Lighten-up List'

Plan for stressful times by creating a "Lighten-up List" of fast, easy, inexpensive things you can do to reduce stress. (Examples: Call a friend, take a deep breath, share a joke, inspect a flower, sniff a sachet of cedar chips, look at a photo of someone you love). When you find your stress building, whip out your list and do something on it to allow your mind to pause, relax and refocus.

11. Have a cathartic whining session

Sometimes we need a chance to vent our feelings of anger, of fear, of how unfair it is, and of how this has derailed the plans we had for our life. It's only after we've had such a catharsis that we can look at our situation objectively.

A cathartic whining session allows the venting without any blowback from innocent parties caught off guard by some vitriolic outburst. Here's how it's done: Find a support group, or a good friend, priest, rabbi, minister or pet you can talk to—not someone you have to be nice and polite with, but someone you can whine, complain, bellyache and cry with. Be sure to choose someone who will not take your words personally, and who won't try to help you problem-solve—someone who will know that you just need a catharsis. Their only role during a cathartic whining session is to be on your side and to agree that you have been wronged. (NOTE: To get a friend to agree to this role, it is only fair that you accord them an equal amount of future time to cathartically whine to you about their own problems.)

Give vent to your feelings—the bigger, more outrageous your complaints the better. NOTHING

is too petty to be fodder for a good catharsis. You do feel put upon; you don't feel cheerful; you, too, hurt all over; you want to snap at your caregiver or at your patient or at a family member who is not helping out. You have financial worries; you're ticked off at Medicaid, or Medicare, or the government in general. Go for it!

Cathartic whining is big. It's exaggerated. Often it is accompanied by a flailing of arms, a nasal voice, and maybe even the banging of a rubber chicken on a counter top. Done well, you will end up with a glimmer of humor and the beginning of a sense of your ability to rise above the situation.

12. Host a whine and cheese party

Is the whole gang going through a tough period? Call them together for a Whine and Cheese Party. Pass around a plate of cheese and allow everyone to whine cathartically, dramatically, about the problem. In stressful times, problems cannot be resolved until the feelings behind them are resolved. A Whine and Cheese Party acknowledges the feelings and clears heads to focus on the issues at hand. I've seen Whine and Cheese Parties work for the caregiver staff, families, patient groups or any combination of the above.

NOTE: Be sure to use high-grade cheeses. They will show that you take your problem seriously, even while taking the whining lightly.

Fondle a Funny File

Have humor on demand

We often get a rush of get-well cards early in an illness. Then they taper off—at about the time when we would really like to get them. This doesn't have to happen if you have created a Funny File. Here are seven quick hints on how to develop and use your Funny File.

1. Develop your Funny File

You have probably already started a Funny File, you just may not recognize it. It's that stack of favorite cards people sent you, that pile of great photos and clippings, and most of the stuff on your refrigerator. Now is the time to organize it into a handy reference folder or, better yet, a loose leaf binder filled with plastic sleeves. There are only a limited number of things you can do when you are sick, or sitting with someone who is, and few of them will bring you chuckles and happy memories. This one will. An added Funny File plus is that when you e-mail a medical update, you will have the jokes or cartoons you need to spice it up.

2. Personalize your Funny File

Keep it subtle and tasteful with a neatly typed label, or go all out with stickers, drawings, cartoons and bright colors. Best yet, commission your kids or grandkids to draw an art masterpiece for the cover. If you are feeling ambitious, create sections for health, work, getting old, birthdays, family— whatever fits your needs.

3. Provide Funny File 'yeast'

Find at least 10 things for your file in the first week. You don't need to continue at this pace, but it does take a little "yeast" to get a file started. Thumbing through old *Reader's Digests*, or the magazines in your doctor's office, can be good jumping off points. Include funny letters from friends, get-well cards, silly awards, headlines and photos that made you laugh, pictures your children drew—whatever tickles you.

4. Include your own material

Make notes about funny things that happen to you (or not so funny ones that you know will seem funny in time). Put these notes in your file to develop later as anecdotes to elicit a chuckle from a caregiver, friend or family member.

5. Feeling frenzied? File it!

Look in your Funny File to help keep things in perspective, to remind yourself of the people who care for you and to reinforce your resilience.

6. Fondle your file

Need the right humor touch for a get-well card, meeting, party or speech? Review your Funny File! You'll be amazed at the fresh ideas you can get just by thumbing through it. I inherited my great-grandmother's Funny File. It is a scrapbook dating back to the 1800s and includes anything, from birthday cards to soup can labels, that made her smile. When I need a shot of creativity, I can always get one by paging through her book.

7. Make your Funny File part of your personal legacy of laughter

A woman at the Edmonds Community College Creative Retirement Institute in Washington State told me that her mother had created a funny file in a loose leaf binder. When she died, the book's format made it easy to distribute the pages as cherished mementos to various family members.

It Won't Kill You to Laugh

Healing with sick humor

No record exists of anyone who actually died laughing. There is, however, lots of anecdotal evidence of shared laughter connecting patient and caregiver in ways that benefit both. Humor often provides the connection that lets family members communicate at important and healing levels.

This is particularly true if you remember that connecting with humor can be as simple as allowing someone else to make you laugh. Real humor is about seeing and sharing the little things—joys, incongruities—that are all around us. As is evident in the following examples, it's not telling a joke so much as it is developing a state of mind.

1. Good riddance to bad rubbish!

Frank A. told me about a woman in his wife's breast cancer support group whose husband divorced her because he just couldn't cope with the idea of her only having one breast.

I asked Frank what he said to the woman. I knew that when Frank's wife kept obsessing over whether her prosthesis was level with her other breast, he had bought her a 3 ft. carpenter's level to check it out! I figured he was the type who would say *something* supportive to this poor woman.

He grinned. "I told her she should consider herself lucky. She had one operation and removed two boobs!"

We should all have such a guy in our corner!

2. Share it with a support group

A woman came up to me after a long-term caregivers conference and told me about her husband. He suffered from Alzheimer's disease that had advanced rather quickly.

She talked about the in-and-out of awareness that such patients often have and how confusing it can be for their caregivers. "If I didn't have a support group," she confessed, "I don't know what I would do. You need people who understand that sometimes it can be funny and sweet and painful—all at the same time."

She shared an incident that happened one night when he was still living at home.

He turned to her in bed and said, "Honey, I know this is hard on you. I hate putting you through this, and I love you all the more for never losing your patience with me."

She quickly responded, "Darling, it's not hard on me. I love you and we've had 50 wonderful years together. When I think of that, this is really no trouble at all."

"But," he cautioned, "as wonderful as you are, I feel obligated to tell you I have a wife in Tacoma, Washington."

She was the wife in Tacoma!

3. Go with the flow

When Pat Wiklund's father was dying, he started getting auditory hallucinations. He would wake up at night swearing at people in his bedroom. Pat, hearing his shouts, would rush in and try unsuccessfully to convince him that there was no one there.

After a week of sleepless nights, she complained to her brother about what was going on. "That's funny," he said "considering Dad is almost deaf."

The next night when the screaming began, Pat rushed in and shouted, "Dad, there is no one here."

"Yes there is," he insisted. "I hear them talking all the @#$%^&*% time!"

"No you don't—you're deaf!"

"Oh, yeah," he said. "I forgot!"

He never again complained about the voices.

4. Join the hallucination

Sometimes joining in an hallucination can provide a bit of fun for you and a bit of relief for your patient.

One morning Pat's father continually

complained that her grandmother (a woman who had died 30 years earlier) was sitting in the room waiting for a ride home.

Later in the day, when Pat came in, he snapped, "Where have you been?"

She simply said, "Taking Grandma home."

"About time!" was his reply, as he relaxed and settled down.

5. Create a memory jar for Oma

Like this elephant, I'll never forget Oma!

David Gear told me this story about his grandmother, Oma.

"I was born while my dad was in the military overseas. He didn't see me until I was 2 years old. My mom went to school and worked a part-time job, so, from the time I landed on this planet, Oma nurtured me like I was her son.

"I never knew how to repay her for all the love and kindness she showed, until one day I heard about a gift called a Memory Jar.

"It was 1990, and Oma's memory was slipping away. I sat down and typed out (in large font) short memories that I had of day-to-day things that my Oma had done for me over the course of a lifetime. I placed all those memories in a glass jar—a glass elephant with a big cork stopper on his back—and gave it to her for Christmas.

"The instructions were to read one a day and place the memory recorded on that piece of paper in another jar until all the slips of paper had been moved from one jar to the next. When the elephant was empty, you would transfer all the memories back into the elephant and begin again.

"My Oma loved those memories so much that she read one every day. She even took them along with her on vacation. If she was gone five days on a trip, she took five memories so she could read one a day.

"During my Oma's memorial service, I got out the memory jar and read a few to our family and friends. I then told the rest of the story that went with that particular memory. There was a huge warm spot in my heart and in my mind and not a dry eye in the house.

"The memory jar is now mine to pass on to someone who would like to carry those memories into the next lifetime."

6. Make a quilt

Marsha is a quilt maker of singular skill. She told me about sitting and talking with her mother while making a quilt from some of her mom's old clothes. They would talk about a dress or blouse and share what stories it held, and then Marsha would cut a square out of it for the quilt.

Sometimes they went beyond clothing to include a piece of a towel or a doily. Marsha said she had never felt so close to her mother as when they sat quietly reminiscing and sewing together. When her mother died, she had a host of wonderful memories.

7. Review the history of clothes

One of the things Sherry and her mother did to while away the caregiving hours was to talk clothes. But not just any clothes. Her mom had clothing going back decades. Sherry would select an intriguing outfit from her mom's closet, and her mom would tell her the story behind the garment.

It might be the story of a party she wore it to; a garden she planted wearing it; a speech she gave; or, in the case of several pairs of slacks with the price tags still on, a crash diet that didn't work! Sherry said she heard entirely new stories about her mom's adventures.

This was especially true of the time after she had left home and started her own family. "When we got together," she said, "everything centered around my kids. Somehow I just figured my folks' life went on hold. I'm a little disconcerted to realize that they were having the time of their life with me out of the house!"

8. Mom's last rites

 Two weeks before Thanksgiving, my dad called. He said that my 83-year-old mother wanted me to come home that weekend. She claimed she was dying and had arranged for the priest to come the next morning to perform the last sacrament for her!

This was a shock, since I had talked to her just a few days before and she had only complained of a stomachache. (Then again, this was a woman who had a mastectomy before she told anyone she had cancer!)

Financially it was also a shock. I was leaving in 90 minutes to catch a plane to Spokane, Washington, giving a half-day workshop the next morning, returning home for two days, then flying to Myrtle Beach, South Carolina for four days of work. That was all of my speaking (and my income) for the rest of the year.

I asked if she was in the hospital. Dad said no, but she had been bedridden for two weeks. He was waiting for the doctor to call. He concluded that I should give my workshop and check back the next afternoon.

When I called the next day, my mom answered. "Are you dying?" I asked.

"No, it's hardly worth it," she sighed. She then complained that the priest was 25 minutes late ("I mean, you don't come late to give someone the last rites!") and that he only spent five minutes performing what should have been a more impressive ceremony.

"After all," she said, "it *is* the last sacrament. I thought there would be a lot more to it. Not only that, the communion wafer was stale—you'd think when it's your last Holy Communion, the least a priest could provide would be a fresh wafer!" She went on to say, "He is actually a nice guy and probably just needs a little feedback. I'll talk to him the next time I see him at Mass."

"You're right," I agreed. "He probably doesn't get much feedback from the parishioners he performs the last rites for! May I please talk to my father!"

Long story short, her blood pressure medication had lowered her salt levels too much, which caused a kind of dementia. Since she already had some disorientation, this made it much worse.

I gave my presentations and got home a week later to find her on her feet, and, though frail, once more, the "salt of the earth." And, yes, she did give a rather surprised priest some feedback!

9. Do something from your life list like . . . nude sunbathing!

Flying to Portland, Oregon, from Des Moines, Iowa, I learned that my seatmate was a nurse returning from spending a month with her 96-year-old mother. She had been relieving her brother who was the principal caregiver. I asked her how it had been, and she said, "My mom is a kick! She still has all her faculties, she just can't navigate very well.

"One day she looked at me with a twinkle in her eye and asked, 'Is anyone coming over today?' Not that I know of, I told her. 'Well, then,' she said, 'Let's do something that has been on my life list for ages . . . nude sunbathing!'

"So picture me with my mother and her double mastectomy, lying out nude on her back deck and both of us doubled up laughing so hard the sun barely had a chance to tan us!"

10. It's a rhap-sody

Maureen Roberts told me about her husband Jim, a classical music buff and retired Navy doctor, and his irrepressible wit in the most difficult of situations.

Jim had been diagnosed with lung and liver cancer, and a regime of chemotherapy was suggested. Warning him about the possible side effects of the chemotherapy, the oncology nurse said, "You may experience a change in your taste." Jim rolled his eyes and winced. "Oh, Lord, you mean I'm going to start liking rap music?"

11. Stop swearing and practice creative cursing

Being sick, or being with someone who is, can be a royal pain. It can make you want to swear at anyone and everyone in the immediate vicinity.

Don't.

Curse them instead!

Swearing, i.e., using bad words, just serves to make most people (including the swearer) angrier. But *cursing*, especially cursing in lofty, over-exaggerated terms, can bring relief to all involved.

Here are a couple of starter curses:

- May your life be as useless as an ashtray on a motorcycle!
- May your pacemaker get vapor lock!
- May an 80-year-old onion farmer give you mouth-to-mouth resuscitation!

12. Laugh 'til it helps!

Linda Keith told me about her grandmother who had Alzheimer's and eventually lived in a long-term care facility.

"On my last trip home before she passed away, my mother and I went to pick Nana up and go shopping at a local mall. At one point I told a funny story, and all three of us laughed and laughed.

"Then Nana turned to me and said: 'I don't know who you are, but you sure are fun!'

"Nana kept laughing and finding fun in life even after she did not know who she was with or where she was.

"Our greatest gift to her at that time in her life was to laugh along with her. And what a gift to me that my last memory of my grandmother is not one of frailty or confusion, but of gut-busting hilarity."

13. Be the master of your craft

Hospice worker Debbie B. told me about a woman in hospice who had only a few weeks to live—and, frankly, was happy, or at least resigned, to her situation.

Her family came regularly to see her, but since no one could actually stay with her, they hired a live-in care provider.

The person they found was into arts and

crafts—in a big way! She got the dying woman involved. It turned out that one thing she really needed was something to live for.

The woman became so involved that her disease went into remission and she moved to assisted living—where she lived for several years.

She actually got good enough that she sold her arts and crafts at local fairs. She laughed that her kids had to wait for their inheritance, but it was bigger because of the sales!

14. Make St. Patrick's Day resolutions full of blarney

Most people don't keep New Year's resolutions because they are "should do" resolutions: I should eat less, exercise more, restrict my computer solitaire playing to three hours a week, etc.

Try, instead to make resolutions you will love to keep. Resolve to do things that will bring more joy into your life. Research abounds about the positive connection between laughter and good health. Make it work for you!

Choose St. Pat's Day, or any other day that's handy, to create your own Humor Resolutions. Here are a few ideas to get you started:

- Resolve to do something silly once a month.
- Laugh at other people's jokes (even if you've heard them before).
- On a weekly, monthly, or whatever-works-for-you basis, write down something funny you see children or pets doing.
- Read the funnies before you go to sleep at night.
- Find one new, upbeat, funny person to hang out with.
- Make a list of the funny things that have happened in your life.
- Make three new funny things happen each week.
- Learn how to draw cartoons.
- Go to the circus.
- See at least four funny plays or movies during the year.
- Start a funny book club.
- Take a class in clowning.
- Put some humor into your Christmas "form" letter.
- Resolve to ask one person a day to tell you something funny.

In short, resolve to do something you *want* to do that will bring more humor into your life in the coming year.

15. Keep them in front of you with a 'Humor Placemat'

Jot down your Humor Resolutions on slips of paper. Then gather up photos, magazine pictures, cartoons, quotes—whatever it takes to remind you of your sense of humor and how you want to expand it over the coming year. Then, get a 12" x 20" piece of smooth, light cardboard and create a collage with all the things you've gathered. When they are all properly glued down on the cardboard, cover your creation with a sheet of laminate paper (sold at most office supply stores).

You have just created a breakfast placemat. Each morning you will get a smile and be reminded of your Humor Resolutions. Intensify the humor/health connection by tucking in some health resolutions as well.

16. Create a running joke

Patients who make someone else's life better feel better themselves. Making someone laugh gives you a sense of power and control.

A home-care nurse told me she was working with a cancer patient who was dying. At the same time, she was training for a marathon that, as luck would have it, ran by his house. They shared small talk about how this was her first marathon, what kind of training regime she was on, and about the hill that faced her right after his house.

On the day of the race, as she ran by his home, there was a big sign in the window cheering her on. She teared up telling me about it. "This man could barely move. He died three days later. How he ever managed to make the sign, much less put it in the window, I will never know. I also will never forget him."

17. Create fun and funny care packages for the patient

It's a bummer lying in a hospital bed day after day. All the more so if you are hurting. Forget the flowers! Bring your sick friend something distracting. A good distraction often

beats drugs when it comes to pain prevention. Create a care package with joke books, funny videos and CDs. Include escape novels with uncomplicated plots and big print (no one wants to work hard when they are sick); photos of friends, family and pets; funny door hangers; and special food treats. Another fun addition is to provide cartoons with the captions removed so the patient (or staff or visitors) can write their own. A doctored-up movie poster can make a great motivational wall hanging. I received one with a svelte leopard-skin-clad weightlifter babe sporting my name on her chest, confirming, "I owe my success to Steven's Hospital Rehab!"

As a real plus, add a box of candy with a sign saying: "For the nurses!" Include instructions that it be placed by the patient's bed. This is a sure fire way to encourage a more attentive nursing staff!

18. Use the technology

Making videos or CDs is no longer the province of the professional.

Several of my National Speaker Association friends put one together for a sick speaker buddy of ours. He was too ill for visitors, so we made the video to let him know he was in our thoughts, hearts and prayers.

We edited a variety of video clips of fellow speakers sending best wishes, acting silly, reading poetry, playing music, singing songs, acting out a get-well play and just plain gossiping. Each clip was no more than five minutes long, which made it easy for him to stop the show when he got tired.

One of the advantages of a composite video is that the friends don't all have to be together. As long as the video clips are in the same format, they can be edited together. The only real trick with this sort of gift is to make sure that you produce your masterpiece in a format that is available to the patient.

19. *Ooh La La.* Monkey business is fun!

My friend M. cared for her 83-year-old mother, Marge Caggiano, in her home during the last years of her life.

One Christmas, M. went on a quest for a gift that might give her mother a little fun, distraction and relief. She remembered stories of good times her mom had spent as a child at her grandmother's home in a suburb of Paris, France. Her grandmother's pet monkey dashed about the house, just out of reach of the delighted child. Later, when Marge had a grandchild of her own, her first gift to him was not a cuddly teddy bear, but a devilish, long-tailed monkey.

And so it was, that in a lifetime of gift giving, the best gift M. ever gave her mother turned out to be a lanky toy monkey with Velcro hands and feet and soulful eyes. Promptly named *La La* (Short for the French *Ooh La La!*), the monkey played a major role in lightening up Marge's final years.

Suiting her Parisian origins, *La La* quickly acquired a glamorous look. She was adorned with real gold and gem castoffs. Hoop earrings became bracelets; studs framed her face. A good friend made a hot pink tutu for *La La* and found a small stylish straw hat. Other outfits from various sources followed—most tracing their origin to Value Village couture.

La La helped Marge bond with caregivers, and the silliness of the whole dress-up game was a distraction from the boredom and pain of a confining illness. Whenever there was a lull in the conversation, *La La* gracefully helped fill it.

On a bad day, M. might enter her mother's room and see *La La's* hands in prayer position. "I hope you noticed we're praying today," was the unspoken message.

When Marge was annoyed with a caregiver, *La La's* arms might be placed in—well, the form of a universal gesture of #%$#^*&*! *you*—one hand at the elbow with the forearm raised. No more was needed to communicate: "That's what *La La* says to that one!"

Sometimes *La La* accompanied Marge to the hospital or to rehab appointments. (She proved invaluable at breaking in new doctors.) Occasionally she stayed for a hospital sleepover. Other times she was only allowed a short visit, with Marge instructing, "Take her home, *La La's* too good for this place."

La La even made a trip from Seattle to Marge's Florida condo. When M. delicately asked Marge if she was going to introduce *La La* to her old friends at the condo, she replied, "Of course!"

Then, noticing her daughter's hesitancy, Marge

laughed and asked, "What are you worried about? That they will think I'm in my second childhood? What do I care? *We're* having *fun,* aren't we?"

Ah—and there was the point and the big lesson for my friend. They sure were—right until the end—having fun.

20. Plan your funeral and go out with a flourish!

"I almost didn't come to Marilyn's funeral. I was afraid of how bummed out I'd be. But I came. Now I'm leaving with this odd mix of elation and gratitude and love. All I can think is: What a gift I've been given—and it's almost as if it's from behind the veil."

This was the feeling of not just one, but, I suspect, hundreds of people who attended Marilyn Brandenberg's funeral on Bainbridge Island, Washington.

Marilyn taught elementary school, was a deacon in her church, raised a couple of great kids, loved life and made a lot of friends.

Suspecting she could sing, she applied for a gig as a vocalist in a jazz band. She proceeded to sing in the Seattle jazz scene for years. Suspecting she'd get smarter if she were with smart people, she joined Mensa.

Yet she impressed you, not because she was brilliant and witty and flashy (which she could be), but because she was centered and comfortable and focused on . . . you.

When she lost her hair to chemo, she plopped on a wig with her vestments and continued teaching in her church. The subtext of her message was to take work seriously and life lightly. To emphasize her point, she ended one sermon by whipping off her normal wig and replacing it with a rainbow Afro wig.

Marilyn died shortly before Christmas—or at least Marilyn's body died then. One of her last contributions to her friends and family was to plan her funeral—right down to leaving a script of what to say when.

To accommodate the 400-500 people in attendance, the French doors along the side of the parish hall were opened and a heated tent added.

Everyone received a package with a red foam clown nose, a smile on a stick, and a bookmark with Marilyn's picture and a favorite quote. A slide show loop depicted Marilyn as girl, mom, teacher, deacon, and friend.

A full tilt boogie choir, backed with two guitars and a clarinet, sang hymns—several of which were written by local people. The service was funny and poignant and spiritual.

Afterward, a caterer provided all of Marilyn's favorite foods, from Chinese barbecue pork to roast turkey. Friends who hadn't seen each other for years swapped stories, assisted by an open bar. An eight-piece jazz band, sporting a large percentage of retired music teachers, provided music. The lead singer (now in his 70s but still able to belt it out) had toured for years with one of the big bands of the 50s.

Marilyn presided over it all.

Cremated.

In an urn on the altar.

With a rainbow Afro wig on top of it.

Life, Love, Laughter and Loss
A few favorite quotations

Laugh more. It's not getting the point of the joke, it's getting the point of joking that really matters.

—*Peter McLaughlin, poet*

~~~~~

Even if there were not a single shred of evidence that laughter affected my biology or health, I would opt for a life filled with laughter. A life absent of laughter is too dreadful to contemplate. Laughter reminds us that we are joyously and joyfully natural beings of nature, not merely surrounded by nature. Laughter reminds us of the ecstatic potential of our existence. Laughter is the primary outer manifestation of joy. Give me a joyful life any day, every day, and I would never need to bother about the "data."

—*Steve Wilson, humorist*

~~~~~

An eye-connecting smile from a stranger can turn a blah day into a Ta-dah day!

~~~~~

I think laughter may be a form of courage. . . . As humans we sometimes stand tall and look into the sun and laugh, and I think we are never more brave than when we do that.
— *Linda Ellerbee, journalist*

Fun is better than winning.

There is no duty we so much underrated as the duty of being happy.
—*Robert Louis Stevenson, author*

O God, help me to believe the truth about myself no matter how beautiful it is.

You can't afford to be disabled in spirit as well as physically. People won't have time for you.
—*Stephen Hawking, theoretical physicist*

Death . . . is no more than passing from one room into another. But there's a difference for me, you know. Because in that other room I shall be able to see.

—Helen Keller, advocate for handicapped

~~~~~

There is life after death, divorce, financial disasters. I know that. The question you must ask yourself is: Is there life before death?

—Lynn Durham, RN, well being coach

~~~~~

People rarely succeed unless they have fun in what they are doing.

—Dale Carnegie, self-improvement trainer

~~~~~

Humor is just another defense against the universe.

—Mel Brooks, comedian, writer, director

~~~~~

It is said that until you have a personal center, you are just a mechanical device. Circumstances push our buttons; if something good happens, we're happy; if something bad happens, we're angry or sad. We can respond or develop a center that allows us to choose our response. When we choose how to respond, we no longer automatically follow old patterns. Instead we begin to ask: "What would love do here?" and we follow that leading.

> —*The Rev. Mary Manin Morrissey, New Thought minister*

I cannot do all the good that the world needs,
But the world needs all the good that I can do.

> —*Jana Stanfield, singer, songwriter*

Laughter is like changing a baby's diaper. It may not solve the problem permanently, but it sure improves the situation for the moment!

I was wise enough to never grow up while fooling most people into believing I had.

—*Margaret Mead, anthropologist*

If I had no sense of humor, I should long ago have committed suicide.

—*Mahatma Gandhi, political and spiritual leader*

Imagination was given to us to compensate for what we are not. A sense of humor was provided to console us for what we are!

~~~~~

In one of the stars I shall be living. In one of them I shall be laughing, and so it will be as if all the stars were laughing when you look at the sky at night.

—*The Little Prince by Antoine de Sainte-Exupery*

~~~~~

When you're depressed, the whole body is depressed, and it translates to the cellular level. The first objective is to get your energy up, and you can do it through play. It's one of the most powerful ways of breaking up hopelessness and bringing energy into the situation.

—*Dr. Carl Simonton, oncologist*

≈≈≈≈≈

For a small child there is no division between playing and learning; between the things he or she does "just for fun" and things that are "educational." The child learns while living and any part of living that is enjoyable is also play.

—*Penelope Leach, Ph.D., parenting expert*

≈≈≈≈≈

The Creator put fun on the earth to mark out correct solutions. He said that if what you're doing isn't fun, it needs re-evaluation. When you have fun in it, chances are you're on the right path.

—*Manitonquat (Medicine Story)*

≈≈≈≈≈

One can discover more about a person in an hour of play than in a year of conversation.
—*Plato, Greek philosopher*

~~~~~

Life is full of little surprises.
—*Pandora,*

~~~~~

The reason we make a long story short is so we can tell another one!

~~~~~

People who enjoy life go the extra smile.

~~~~~

With the possible exception of Elvis, nothing lasts forever.

~~~~~

The best cure for hypochondria is to forget about your own body and get interested in someone else's.
—*Goodman Ace, comedian*

~~~~~

You can observe a lot, just by watching.
    —*Yogi Berra, baseball player*

Until one has loved a pet, a part of their soul has yet to be awakened.

Optimism and humor are the grease and glue of life. Without both of them we would have never survived our captivity.
    —*Philip Butler, Vietnam POW*

When you are having fun, you are helping others. When you are not having fun, and telling yourself that you're helping others, you are not helping them or yourself.
    —*Seth (channeled by Jane Roberts)*

When we are hurt, there is no sweeter revenge than to forgive.

Let the surgeon take care to regulate the whole regimen of the patient's life for joy and happiness, allowing his relatives and special friends to cheer him, and by having someone tell him jokes.
—*Dr. Henri de Mondeville, surgeon*

If I wait to be happy, I'll wait forever. If I choose to be happy now, I'll be happy forever.

Laughter is a holy thing. It is as sacred as music and silence and solemnity, maybe more sacred. Laughter is like a prayer, like a bridge over which creatures tiptoe to meet each other. Laughter is like mercy; it heals. When you can laugh at yourself, you are free.
—*The Rev. Ted Loder, social activist*

While you are laughing, you're not old and you're never sick.
—*Dr. Bernie Segal, oncologist*

A laughing heart is more courageous than a serious one. A serious heart doubts, hesitates, thinks twice. The laughing one is the heart of the gambler; he simply jumps in!
—*Osho, Indian spiritual leader*

≈≈≈≈≈

We are here on earth to do good to others. What the others are here for, I don't know.
—*W.H. Auden, poet*

≈≈≈≈≈

See with your heart . . . it never needs glasses.

≈≈≈≈≈

The nicest thing about a laugh is that so much of you has a good time!

≈≈≈≈≈

You mustn't be serious, my dear one, it's just what they want.
—*Elyot in "Private Lives" by playwright Noel Coward*

≈≈≈≈≈

Death Asked Me to Dance
Lynn Durham

Death asked me to dance.
And what could I say?
I suppose I could say no,
But he'd take me anyway.

My life has been good.
I hope I've brought joys.
It seems hard to go
And leave all my boys.

Actually I won't though,
It may look like I'm gone
But I've stepped through the veil
And have greeted the dawn.

Know that I'm there
Though the mists obscure view,
I'm singing and dancing
And watching over you.

For love has no boundaries,
It reaches through space.
As quick as a thought,
We're embraced in one place.

Know that I'm with you,
I'll never be far.
Until you will join me
And swing on our star.

Share your stories!

Let me know how you have applied the information in this book and/or tell me how you are using humor in your long-term care situation.

E-mail your story to me at:

Patt@FUNdamentallySpeaking.com

If you include some photos, I'll make sure they get posted on my website at:

www.FUNdamentallySpeaking.com

About the Author

A combination of health care clients, aging parents, and a realization that she, herself, was getting no younger, brought Dr. Patt Schwab into the world of long-term care. Her 20 years speaking about humor in the workplace caused her to look for, and find, the humor in long-term care settings.

In her other life, Dr. Schwab owns FUNdamentally Speaking, an international speaking and training company that believes in putting the "FUN" before "Da Mental!" She shows midlevel managers and front-line staff how to use humor to increase rapport, resilience, and the bottom line.

Her programs are packed with laughter, insight, and practical tips for: managing people, coping with change, and enriching work and home life.

Patt combines years of hands-on management, teaching and training with work as a full time professional speaker in Europe, Canada and the USA. Her programs range from keynotes to full day seminars.

Dr. Schwab encourages her audience to look inside themselves for a humorous perspective on life's problems and challenges.

She holds academic degrees in History, Student Personnel, and Administration. Her doctoral thesis, on teambuilding, was titled, "People Support What They Help Create." She also holds the highest earned designation awarded by the National Speakers Association, the CSP, or Certified Speaking Professional.

Liven up your next meeting with a motivational humorist focused on helping you use humor to increase resilience, rapport, and the bottom line!

Some of Patt's popular presentations include:

Leave a Mark — Not a Stain!
(What every manager needs to know about humor in the workplace)

Creating a Legacy of Laughter
(How to invest in a legacy of fun)

When Hell Freezes Over—Ice S.K.A.T.E!
(Mastering change and adversity)

When LIFE Freezes Over—Ice S.K.A.T.E!
(Bringing humor to long term care)

S/He Who Laughs . . . Lasts!
(Humor as an interpersonal skill and workplace tool)

If You Don't Pause, Nothing Worthwhile Will Catch Up With You
(How to feel significant, competent and appreciated in a fast-paced world)

What If The Hokey Pokey IS What It's All About!
(Writing the next chapter of your life)

For a presentation tailored to your event and your organization, contact Patt in Seattle, Washington.
VOICE: 206-525-1031
FAX: 206-525-8960
E-mail: patt@FUNdamentallySpeaking.com

Also by Dr. Patt Schwab

Creating a Legacy of Laughter
60 Easy Ways to Add Humor to Your Daily Life

Leave a Mark, Not a Stain!
What Every Manager Needs to Know About Using Humor in the Workplace

What if the Hokey Pokey IS What It's All About?
A Workbook for Writing the Next Chapter of Your Life

Humor Us
America's Funniest Humorists on the Power of Laughter

All books by Dr. Schwab and a variety of Humor Tips and articles (many for free) are available at:
     www.FUNdamentallySpeaking.com

Where can I get a rubber chicken?

A Superior One—not one of those cheesy, fall-apart-with-the-first-womp-on-a-tabletop ones!

Funny you should ask!
If you want a quality rubber chicken (Yep, there actually are quality differences between them!), or any of an ever-changing variety of rubber chicken products, go to: www.FUNdamentallySpeaking.com